慢吞吞的泰迪

【美】露西·瑞切·潘纳◎著
【美】吉奥雅·法蒙吉◎绘
范晓星◎译

天津出版传媒集团
新蕾出版社

献给罗伦·麦克·琼斯。

——露西·瑞切·潘纳

献给米兰和奥斯卡。

——吉奥雅·法蒙吉

图书在版编目 (CIP) 数据

慢吞吞的泰迪/(美)潘纳(Penner,L.R.)著;
(美)法蒙吉(Fiammenghi,G.)绘;范晓星译.--天津:
新蕾出版社,2016.7(2024.12重印)
(数学帮帮忙·互动版)
书名原文:Slowpoke
ISBN 978-7-5307-6401-5

Ⅰ.①慢… Ⅱ.①潘…②法…③范… Ⅲ.①数学-
儿童读物Ⅳ.①01-49

中国版本图书馆CIP数据核字(2016)第078049号

津图登字:02-2015-222

出版发行:天津出版传媒集团
新蕾出版社
http://www.newbuds.com.cn
地　　址:天津市和平区西康路35号(300051)
出 版 人:马玉秀
电　　话:总编办(022)23332422
发行部(022)23332679　23332351
传　　真:(022)23332422
经　　销:全国新华书店
印　　刷:天津新华印务有限公司
开　　本:787mm×1092mm　1/16
印　　张:3
版　　次:2016年7月第1版　2024年12月第19次印刷
定　　价:12.00元

地址:天津市和平区西康路35号
电话:(022)23332351　邮编:300051

无处不在的数学

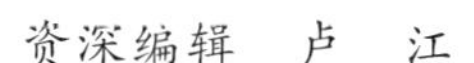

资深编辑　卢　江

人们常说“兴趣是最好的老师”，有了兴趣，学习就会变得轻松愉快。数学对于孩子来说或许有些难，因为比起语文，数学显得枯燥、抽象，不容易理解，孩子往往不那么喜欢。可许多家长都知道，学数学对于孩子的成长和今后的生活有多么重要。不仅数学知识很有用，学习数学过程中获得的数学思想和方法更会影响孩子的一生，因为数学素养是构成人基本素质的一个重要因素。但是，怎样才能让孩子对数学产生兴趣呢？怎样才能激发他们兴致勃勃地去探索数学问题呢？我认为，让孩子读些有趣的书或许是不错的选择。读了这套“数学帮帮忙”，我立刻产生了想把它们推荐给教师和家长朋友们的愿望，因为这真是一套会让孩子爱上数学的好书！

这套有趣的图书从美国引进，原出版者是美国资深教育专家。每本书讲述一个孩子们生活中的故事，由故事中出现的问题自然地引入一个数学知识，然后通过运用数学知识解决问题。比如，从帮助外婆整理散落的纽扣引出分类，从为小狗记录藏骨头的地点引出空间方位等等。故事素材全部来源于孩子们的真实生活，不是童话，不是幻想，而是鲜活的生活实例。正是这些发生在孩子身边的故事，让孩子们懂得，数学无处不在并且非常有用；这些鲜活的实例也使得抽象的概念更易于理解，更容易激发孩子学习数学的兴趣，让他们逐渐爱上数学。这样的教育思想和方法与我国近年来提倡的数学教育理念是十分吻合的！

这是一套适合5~8岁孩子阅读的书，书中的有趣情节和生动的插画可以将抽象的数学问题直观化、形象化，为孩子的思维活动提供具体形象的支持。如果亲子共读的话，家长可以带领孩子推测情节的发展，探讨解决难题的办法，让孩子在愉悦的氛围中学到知识和方法。

值得教师和家长朋友们注意的是，在每本书的后面，出版者还加入了“互动课堂”及“互动练习”，一方面通过一些精心设计的活动让孩子巩固新学到的数学知识，进一步体会知识的含义和实际应用；另一方面帮助家长指导孩子阅读，体会故事中数学之外的道理，逐步提升孩子的阅读理解能力。

我相信孩子读过这套书后一定会明白，原来，数学不是烦恼，不是包袱，数学真能帮大忙！

泰迪·克雷默跑得不太快。他爸爸跑得快多了，妈妈也一样。至于哥哥乔伊，就更别提了！泰迪只能看见乔伊闪过拐角的脚后跟。

别的孩子都叫泰迪“小蜗牛”，连他最好的朋友罗伯特也这样叫他。

排队买午餐的时候，泰迪总在队末。

打棒球的时候，他总是出局。

去海边游泳，泰迪总是最后一个下水。

泰迪在任何事上从没得过第一名。

有一天,泰迪所在的班级去动物园游玩。泰迪最后一个上车,所以只好坐在石老师身边。

参观了蛇馆和企鹅馆之后，大家都去买冰激凌吃。泰迪又是最后一个。他最喜欢的什锦水果口味的冰激凌已经卖光了。

后来，全体同学抓紧时间排队到宠物乐园去。等到泰迪去喂小动物时，小动物们都已经吃饱了。

这一天真是太倒霉了。

“我老是慢吞吞的，我自己都烦了。”回到学校，泰迪对罗伯特抱怨道。

“那你干吗不快点儿呢？”罗伯特说，“每天跑步吧！集中精神，别老走神儿！”

“好吧，我考虑考虑。”泰迪回答。

泰迪和家人说了罗伯特的建议。

“我知道你能做到！”妈妈说。

“问题是，”哥哥乔伊说，“你总是慢吞吞的，还老东张西望。”

“别总磨磨蹭蹭的。”爸爸说，“你要集中注意力，一心一意，勇往直前！”

啊哈，泰迪心里有了主意。

星期一，泰迪从家跑到校车站。

半路上，他对修剪树枝的工人挥手打招呼。

他看见路上有枚硬币，就弯腰捡起来。

遇到一条白色的小狗，他便过去亲热一番。

一路上他花了 6 分钟，又是最后到校车站的，跟往常一样。

星期二和星期三泰迪还是这样。到了星期四，他出发就晚了，所以只好抓紧时间，不然就赶不上校车了。他上气不接下气地跑到车站。“才4分钟我就跑到这儿了！”他对罗伯特说，“比平时快了2分钟呢。”

“哇！怎么回事？”罗伯特问。

“我今天起晚了，就没磨磨蹭蹭。”泰迪说，“1秒钟都没浪费。”

他们下了校车，泰迪跑进学校，一位老师拦住他，又是石老师。

“不能跑。”石老师说，“要慢慢走。”

哈哈！还是第一次有人这样对泰迪说呢。

泰迪感觉美美的。

泰迪决定只要有时间就跑步。他每天下午都绕着街道跑 5 圈，总共 20 分钟。

史蒂夫和莎拉朝他喊：“我们做了饼干，你要不要来一块？”

“好的。”泰迪说，“可是我不能停。”

史蒂夫跑上前递给泰迪一块饼干。

“谢了！”泰迪说，“我最爱吃香蕉巧克力饼干了！”他马不停蹄地往前跑。

泰迪遇上了可爱的三胞胎宝宝，可他没停下来看。

就连看到消防车停到了李先生的家门口，他也没去凑热闹。

星期六，妈妈要到快捷超市买东西，于是泰迪跑步去买。

以前，泰迪要花 20 分钟才能到超市。现在，他只用了 12 分钟，剩下 8 分钟他在超市看了《跑步爱好者》杂志。

开始	结束
11:10 →	11:22

巧手煎饼
猫世界
最爱巧克力
完美花园
钱币
收藏家
跑步爱好者

回家的路上，泰迪遇见哥哥乔伊。

“你是为了比赛而练习吗？”乔伊问。

泰迪猛地停住脚步：“什么比赛？”

“你不知道啊，就是为图书馆募捐的比赛啊。”乔伊说，“妈妈给咱们两个都报名了。”

“我要参加比赛了?!”泰迪惊呆了。“如果我跑最后一名呢? ”他问乔伊。

“别担心。”乔伊说,“只要跑到终点就是胜利。”

可我不想当最后一名啊,泰迪心想,我还得拼命练习。

课间休息时间是 40 分钟。许多孩子在玩球，还有的同学玩攀登架。泰迪没有玩。他跑步。他跑得飞快，路边的树从耳边一闪而过。他跑了 25 分钟。

“哦！”泰迪说，“今天跑得差不多了。”

泰迪在饮水器旁停下，一位老师走过来，又是石老师。唉！

可石老师没有生气，而是赞许地说："你跑得可真快呀！"

可能是真的，泰迪想，也许我就是能跑得特别快。要是我比赛时再努力些的话，说不定还能赢得冠军呢！前提是我要再多多练习，更加专心。

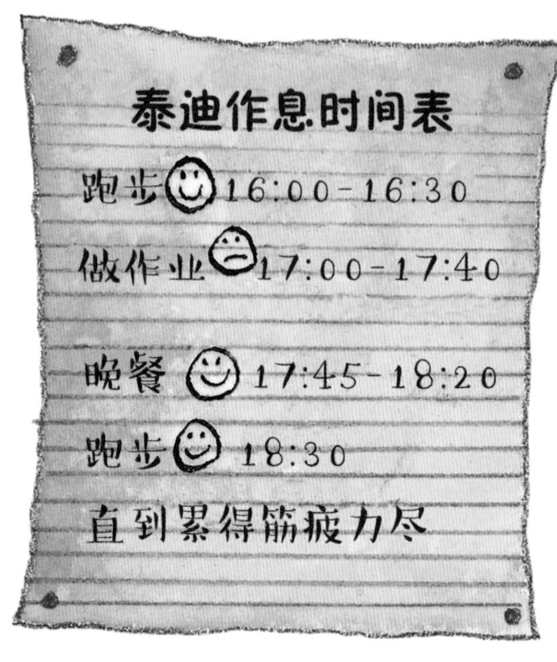

以前，泰迪每天放学后跑 20 分钟，现在变成了 30 分钟。

他非常专心，做事一心一意，40 分钟就做完所有的作业。

泰迪吃晚饭花了35分钟，餐巾上一点儿都没弄脏。

晚饭后，他又跑步去了。他还倒着跑呢！

妈妈叫了他两次，他才回家！

终于,比赛的日子到了!泰迪的那组已站在起跑线旁。泰迪在第 5 跑道,皮特在第 4 跑道。皮特可是学校里有名的“飞毛腿”。

泰迪往旁边看了一眼。皮特在系鞋带,这已经是第 3 次了!他是不是紧张啦?

泰迪也把自己的鞋带重新系了一遍。也许我会赢呢，他心想，我一定要试试！

泰迪蹲下身，等待哨声。

哨声响了，泰迪冲了出去。他超过了几个同学，可前面还有好几个呢。

他加快了脚步。前面只有3个人了。

“专心！”泰迪告诉自己。他超过皮特了。

可皮特追了上来。泰迪又超过了他。他俩几乎并驾齐驱。

泰迪率先冲过了终点线。他得了第一名！

泰迪的家人跑上来。罗伯特也跟在后面。
“祝贺你！”大家欢呼。
“你跑得真快！”妈妈说。
“你这些天真没白练！”爸爸说。
“你很专注！”罗伯特说。
“你真了不起！”乔伊说。

“我？”泰迪说，“哇！”

你们猜怎么着？从那以后，再也没有人叫泰迪“小蜗牛”了。

他有了个新外号——“小猎豹”！

如何计算时间段

时间段是指从起始时刻到结束时刻之间的时长。

你能算出乔伊几点结束跑步的吗？

提示：从 2:40 开始计起，累加 40 分钟。

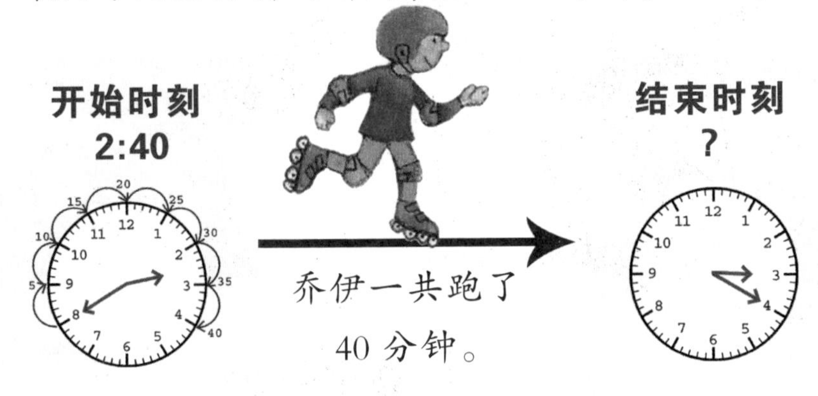

答案：3:20

你能算出泰迪跑了多长时间吗？

提示：用结束时刻减去起始时刻就能得出答案啦！

答案：35 分钟

亲爱的家长朋友，请您和孩子一起完成下面这些内容，会有更大的收获哟！

提高阅读能力

- 阅读封面，包括书名、作者等信息。让孩子说说“慢吞吞”是什么意思呢？平时自己做事情也慢吞吞吗？
- 读过故事以后，同孩子讨论“磨蹭”和“专心”这两个词。看看故事里的泰迪是如何从做事磨蹭变成做事专心的。
- 假设故事中全班同学去动物园游玩时，泰迪没有磨蹭，那么会有什么不同？

巩固数学概念

• 准备一个玩具钟表，让孩子认知时间，并理解“1 小时等于 60 分钟”的换算概念。让孩子用玩具钟表依次摆出第 11 页中泰迪离开家的时刻及到达校车站的时刻，再摆出第 13 页的两个时刻。

• 再次阅读第 20 页的文字，课间休息从 9:30 开始，长达 40 分钟，那么由此推断打上课铃时应该是几点？

生活中的数学

• 选择安全的公园或者游戏场，为孩子设置好起点和终点，让孩子开始跑步。记录下孩子跑步开始和跑步结束的时刻，然后请孩子自己计算一共用了多长时间。

• 做一张周计划表。请孩子合理计划每天都进行哪些活动，每项活动需要多长时间。鼓励孩子在各项活动之间预留出一些时间。请孩子按计划表执行。

• 和孩子讨论下每天在哪些事情上会浪费时间，如果想要缩短时间的话，具体需要怎么做。

互动练习

你能将表示相同时间的钟表用线连起来吗？

1:00

5:00

6:00

8:00

11:00

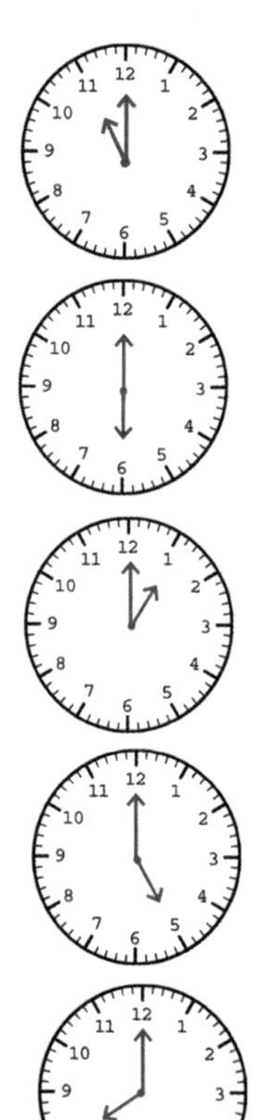

互动练习2

泰迪制订了新的作息时间表,你能说出每一项活动他都用了多长时间吗?

互动练习3

邮递员叔叔一天一共有三次取信时间，分别是：8:40、14:00 和 18:30。根据这条线索，试着回答下面的问题：

①第 2 次和第 1 次的取信间隔时间为多长？

②第 3 次和第 2 次的取信间隔时间为多长？

③泰迪和妈妈去游乐园了，但他有一封信打算今天寄出。他们 17:20 从游乐园里出来，需要 1 小时 20 分钟才能到达距离最近的邮筒，那么泰迪能赶在今天将信寄出吗？

判断下列说法正确吗？

①晚上 10 时就是 22 时。(　)

②8:00–18:10 经过了 10 个小时。(　)

③21 时就是晚上 8 时。(　)

④明明每天 7 小时起床。(　)

⑤24 时就是 24 个小时。(　)

泰迪感冒了，他想吃完感冒药后再休息。以下是吃药前需要做的几件事及所需要的时间。请帮泰迪想想，怎样安排才能尽早休息。

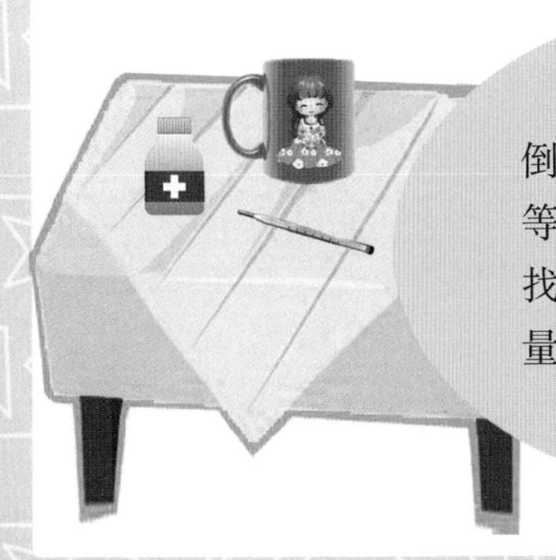

倒开水 1 分钟
等开水变成温水 6 分钟
找感冒药 1 分钟
量体温 5 分钟

互动练习6

试着完成下面的填空题,如果你觉得太难,可以拿一块表来帮助你答题。

①钟面上时针指着 8,分针指着 12,是(　)时整。

②钟面上时针指着 6,分针指着 12,是(　)时整。这时时针和分针在一条直线上。

③钟面上时针走过 7, 分针从 12 起走了 30 个小格(每小格代表 1 分钟),这一时刻是(　)时(　)分。

④时针在 9 和 10 之间,分针指着 5,是(　)时(　)分。

互动练习7

根据常识，在圆圈内填入“＞”“＜”“＝”号。

①1 小时○60 分钟

②1 分钟○100 秒

③10 分钟○1 小时

④4 小时○4 分钟

互动练习 1：

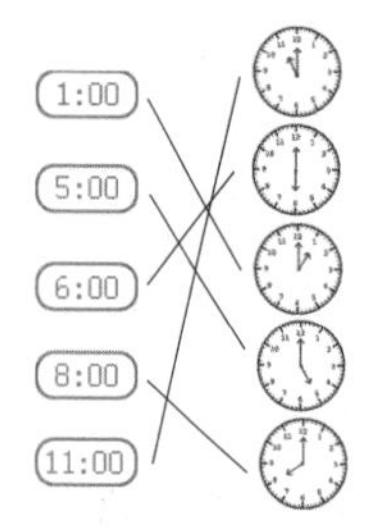

互动练习 2：

整理房间：20 分钟
写作业：30 分钟
跑步：30 分钟
读书：40 分钟
吃晚饭：40 分钟

互动练习 3：

①5 小时 20 分钟
②4 小时 30 分钟
③不能

互动练习 4：

①√
②×
③×
④×
⑤×

互动练习 5：

先倒开水，在开水变成温水的过程中，找感冒药和量体温。

互动练习 6：

①8
②6
③7　30
④9　5

互动练习 7：

①=
②<
③<
④>

（习题设计：何　晨）

Slowpoke

Teddy Kramer wasn't very fast. His dad could run much faster. His mother could too. His brother, Joe—forget it! All Teddy ever saw were the bottoms of Joe's shoes disappearing around the corner.

The other kids called Teddy "Slowpoke". Even his best friend, Robert, called him "Slowpoke".

Teddy was always the last kid on line.

He always got tagged out.

At the beach Teddy was always the last one in the water.

Teddy was never first at anything.

One day Teddy's class went to the zoo. Teddy was last on the bus, so he had to sit next to a teacher—Mr. Stone.

After they saw the snakes and the penguins, everybody went for ice cream. Teddy was last again. They were out of his favorite flavor, Frooti Tooti.

Then the class hurried to line up for the petting zoo. Teddy was the last one to get to feed the animals. They weren't hungry anymore.

It was a terrible day.

"I'm sick of being a slowpoke," Teddy told Robert when they got back to school.

"Why don't you try to get faster?" said Robert. "Practice running every day. And, really concentrate—no daydreaming!"

"Okay, I'll think about it." Teddy said.

Teddy told his family about Robert's idea.

"I know you can do it," said his mom.

"The problem is," his brother Joe said, "you're always slowing down and looking around."

"Dawdling," said his father. "Try to concentrate on getting where you're going."

Hmmm, thought Teddy.

On Monday Teddy ran from his house to the bus stop.

On the way he waved to the tree doctor.

He picked up a quarter lying on the street.

He petted a big white dog.

It took him six minutes. He was last on the bus—as usual.

Teddy was last on Tuesday and Wednesday, too. On Thursday he left late. He really had to rush—or miss the bus. He was panting when he got there."I made it in four minutes!" he told Robert."Two minutes faster than usual."

"Wow, how come?" Robert asked.

"I was late, so I didn't dawdle," said Teddy. "Not for a second."

When they got off the bus, Teddy ran into school. A teacher stopped him. It was Mr. Stone.

"No running here," Mr. Stone said. "Slow down."

Ha! That was the first time anyone ever said that to Teddy.

He liked it.

Teddy decided to run whenever he could. Every afternoon he ran up and down the block five times. It took him twenty minutes.

Steven and Sara called to him, "We made cookies. Do you want one?"

"Yes," Teddy said. "But I can't stop."

Steven ran up and gave him a cookie.

"Thanks," Teddy said. "I love banana chip cookies!" He kept on running.

Teddy didn't stop to look at the new baby triplets.

He didn't even stop when a fire engine pulled into Mr. Lee's driveway.

On Saturday his mom needed something at the Quick Mart, so Teddy ran to get it.

It used to take Teddy 20 minutes to get to the store. Now he could run there in 12 minutes. He used the extra eight minutes to look at Runner magazine.

On the way home Teddy ran into Joe.

"Are you practicing for the race?" Joe asked him.

Teddy stopped short. "What race?"

"You know—to raise money for the library," Joe said. "Mom signed up both of us."

I'm in a race! Teddy thought. He gulped. "Suppose I come in last?" he asked Joe.

"Don't worry," said Joe. "It's finishing the race that counts."

But I don't want to be last, Teddy thought. I've got to practice even more.

Recess was 40 minutes long. Some kids played ball. Others climbed the monkey bars. Teddy didn't play. He ran. He ran so fast, the trees were a blur. He ran for 25 minutes.

"Whew!" said Teddy. "That's it for now."

Teddy stopped at the water fountain. A teacher came up to him. It was Mr. Stone—again. Uh—oh.

But Mr. Stone wasn't mad. "You're fast," he said.

Maybe it's true, Teddy thought. Maybe I am fast. Maybe I can even win the race if I try very hard...if I practice and concentrate.

He used to run for 20 minutes every day after school. Now he ran for 30 minutes.

He concentrated so hard he finished all his homework in 40 minutes.

Teddy ate dinner in 35 minutes—and he didn't get a single spot on his napkin!

After dinner he ran some more. He even ran backwards!

He didn't come in until his mom called—twice!

Finally—it was race day! Teddy's group lined up. Teddy (number 5) was next to Peter Jack (number 4). He was the fastest runner around.

Teddy looked over. Peter Jack was tying his shoelaces for the third time! Was he nervous?

Teddy retied his own shoelaces. "Maybe I can win," he said to himself. "I'm sure going to try!"

Teddy crouched down and waited for the whistle.

When the whistle blew, Teddy leaped forward. He passed some kids but there were still plenty in front of him.

He ran faster. Only three kids were ahead of him now.

"Concentrate!" Teddy told himself. He was gaining on Peter Jack.

Peter Jack pulled ahead. Then Teddy pulled ahead. They were almost side by side.

Then Teddy crossed the finish line. He had won the race!

Teddy's family ran up to him. Robert was right behind them.

"Congratulations!" everyone shouted.

"You were very fast," his mom said.

"All that practice sure paid off!" his dad added.

"You concentrated!" Robert told him.

"You're awesome," said Joe.

"Me?" said Teddy. "Wow!"

Guess what? No one called Teddy "Slowpoke" after that.

He had a new nickname—"Slow down!"